BODY ARMOUR

Which two of these Ankylos
are the same?

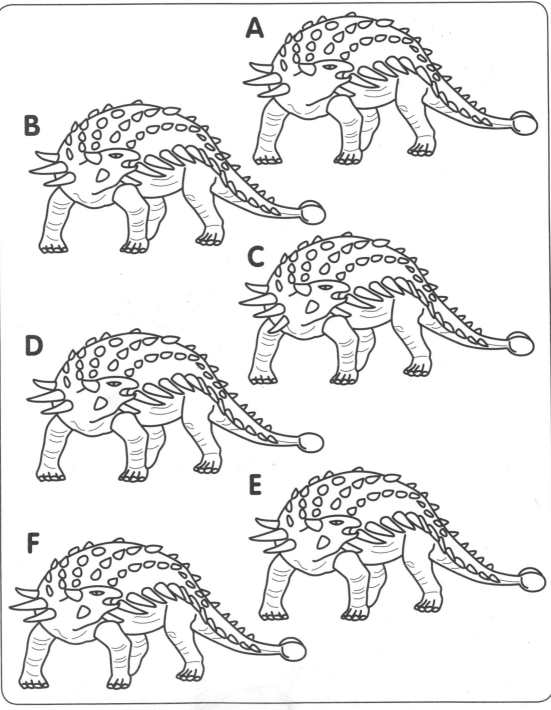

ALL AT SEA

This prehistoric watery world needs some colour adding.

MEMORY TEST

Look back at the picture on page 3 for one minute.
Now answer these questions without cheating!

1. Where is the creature that looks like a shark – top, middle or bottom?

2. How many flippers are showing on the top creature?

3. Which side of the picture are the plants: left or right?

4. How many sets of air bubbles are there?

5. Which of the creatures has its teeth showing?

6. How many schools of small fish are there?

7. Which way is the middle creature facing – to your left or right?

8. How many gills does the shark-like creature have?

BONE YARD

How many of the different bones can you count in this archaeological dig?

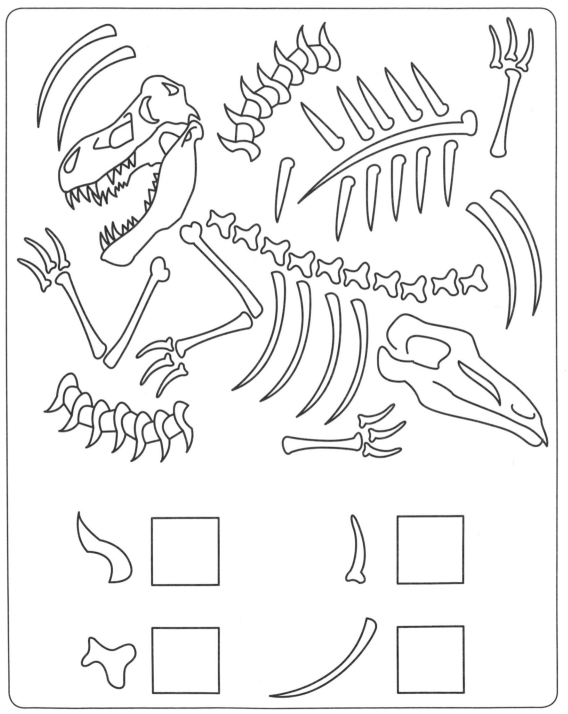

ON THE PROWL

Watch out - this T-rex looks hungry. Colour him in, quick!

BRAINY BEAST

Velociraptor was one of the cleverest dinosaurs, but can you help it get through the grid using numbers from the 7 times table?

START →

6	37	18	27	47	50	9
14	26	39	67	44	57	24
35	48	29	54	25	17	53
7	21	63	42	70	30	45
16	34	40	66	49	23	36
11	25	61	55	28	56	14
41	52	33	12	43	51	42
10	46	19	26	38	20	21

FINISH

THUMBS UP

Which of these Iguanodons has the right answer to the sum

$$100 - 63 + 2.5 + 10.5 - 5 = ?$$

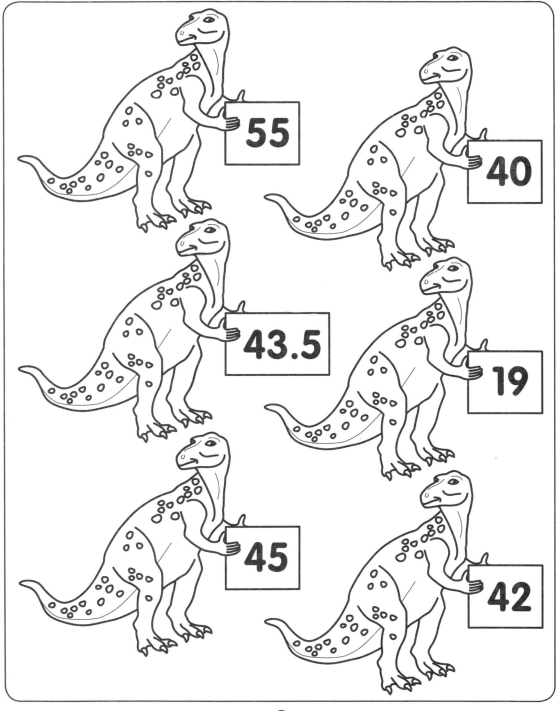

DINO DICTIONARY

Can you find all ten listed words
hidden in the grid?

```
O S S J U R A S S I C O
P R E H I S T O R I C L
R E T E P A S S I C R O
E H E R X P R E D E E N
F J P A S T E R P T T T
P U R C S S I T P A A E
R R E R O V I N R A C R
E F S I T L B C C R E T
D C O S E H S I F T O S
A A H S H X I S V O U S
T R I A S S I C T O S O
O E R O V I B R E H R F
R C A R N I L J U R A E
C R E T I L E P R E D V
```

CARNIVORE   CRETACEOUS   EXTINCT

FOSSIL   HERBIVORE

JURASSIC   PREDATOR   PREHISTORIC

REPTILE   TRIASSIC

10

FEELING ODD

Which of these Triceratops skeletons
is the odd one out?

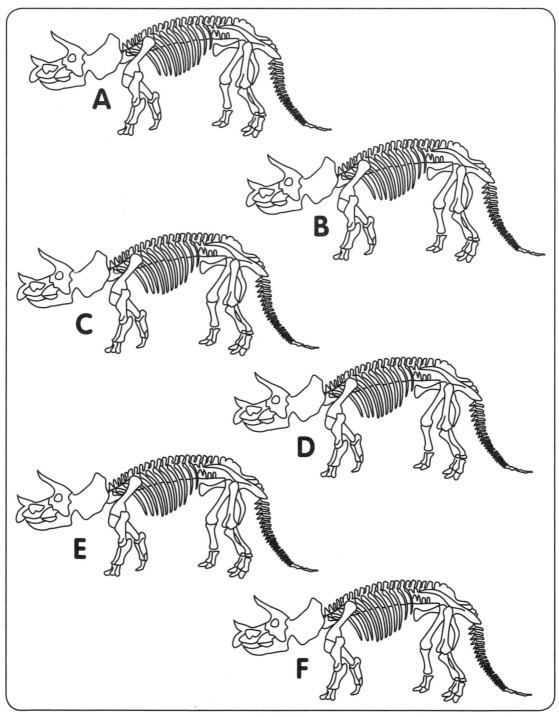

A

B

C

D

E

F

ON TWO LEGS

Colour these dinosaurs to show off their amazing patterns.

THE NAME GAME

Use the clue letters to fit the dino-names into the grid.
The circled letters will spell another dinosaur for you.

		R						
		L		S	◯			
	T		H					◯
E			◯					
	T				◯			N
		I				◯		
		◯						
◯	I	A						

ALLOSAURUS   **ALTIRHINUS**

BAROSAURUS   **DRYOSAURUS**

EOTYRANNUS   **PTERANODON**

UTAHRAPTOR   **XIAOSAURUS**

PRIME-ORDIAL

Use the dinosaur eggs containing prime numbers
to spell the name of a fast, lightweight predator.

___ ___ ___ ___ ___ ___ ___ ___ ___

DOTTY DINOS

Join the dots to find out what kind
of dinosaur is hiding.

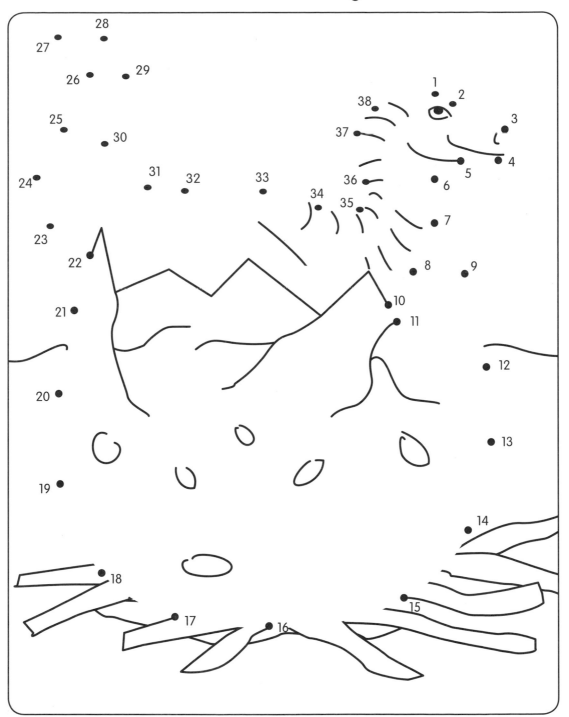

DINO BABIES

Colour in this mother Maiasaura and her nest of babies.

FOUR-A-SAURUS

Use the numbers from the four times table
to guide the Stegosaurus through the forest.

IN THE SHADE

Styracosaurus had long sharp horns on its head
– watch out! Which silhouette matches the main picture?

LONG AGO

Fill in the numbers following the instructions. The answer in the top dino egg is how many million years ago Argentinosaurus was around.

The number in each egg is the total of the two numbers below it.

For example, the shaded number is 3 because 1 + 2 = 3.

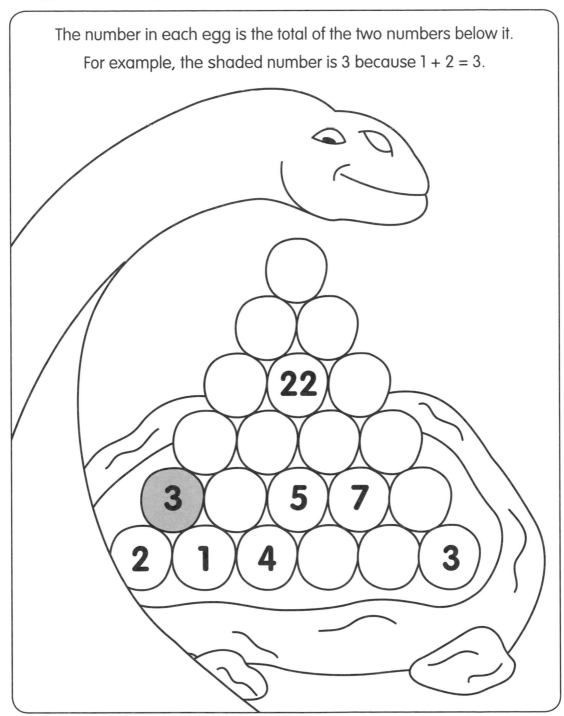

CODE CRACKER

Uncode the symbols on this dinosaur's spikes
to find out what it is called.

A = 💧	I = ⌘	Q = ♈
B = ✡	J = ⊠	R = ✓
C = ✋	K = ❖	S = ⚲
D = 🏳	L = ☮	T = ⇨
E = ☺	M = ○	U = ▲
F = ◆	N = ☆	V = ❄
G = ✠	O = ☼	W = ❋
H = ▢	P = ●	X = ✳

MIGHTY MEAT EATER

Are you brave enough to colour the scary Spinosaurus?

STEGO-TEST

Which group of letters cannot be unscrambled
to spell STEGOSAURUS correctly?

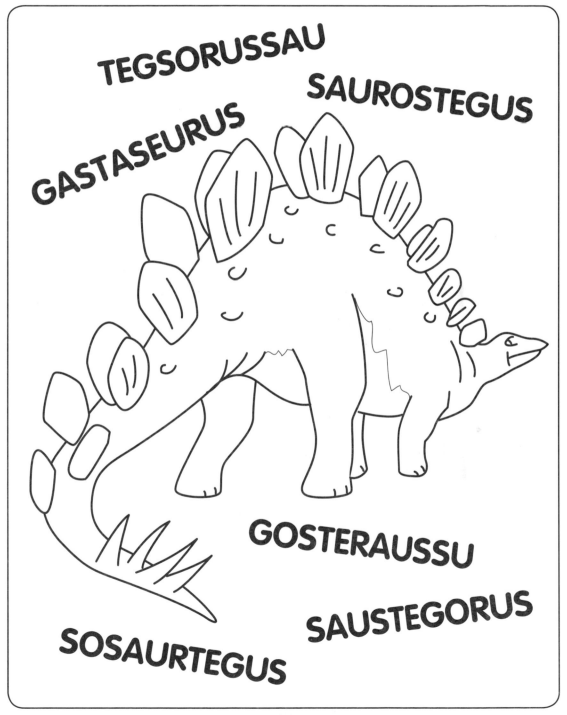

TEGSORUSSAU

SAUROSTEGUS

GASTASEURUS

GOSTERAUSSU

SAUSTEGORUS

SOSAURTEGUS

JIG-SAWRUS

This jigsaw is of a Giganotosaurus!
Which of the three pieces finished the picture?

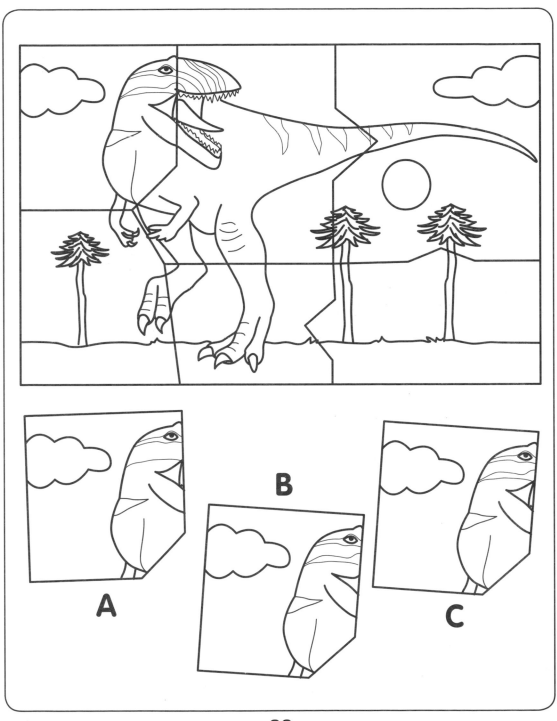

ARMOURED BEAST

This Ankylosaurus is ready for battle – but you can add some colour first.

WHY OH WHY?

Answer the joke by colouring all the squares with the letters
D, N or L and seeing what letters are left.

Why did the
dinosaur bounce?

D	I	D	L	N	D	T	L	N	L
L	L	D	N	D	L	N	N	N	D
W	D	N	L	A	L	S	L	D	D
N	L	N	L	D	L	D	N	N	L
L	A	D	L	D	N	D	L	L	N
L	D	L	D	D	L	N	L	L	N
L	D	T	N	R	D	L	N	N	I
D	C	L	D	L	E	N	R	N	A
L	L	D	N	D	L	D	L	L	N
D	H	L	O	P	N	S	L	L	N

RIGHT TRILOBITE

Use the letters on the trilobites swimming to the right to spell the name of someone who is very interested in dinosaurs.

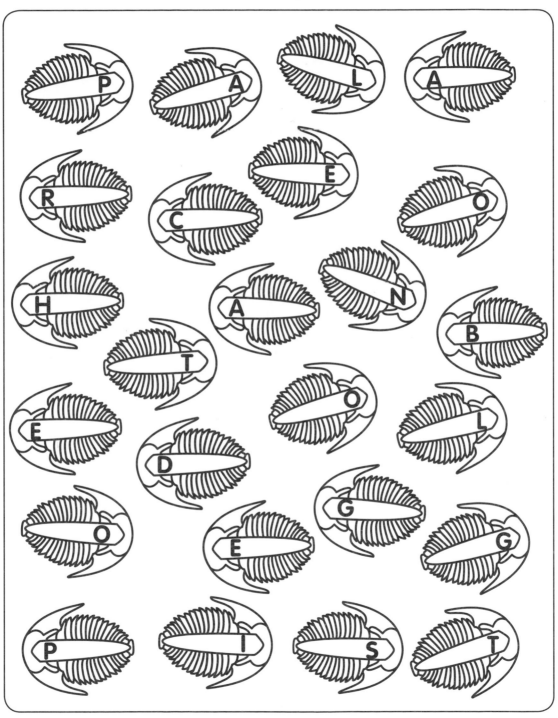

EARLY APPEARANCE

Plateosaurus was an early plant-eater. Can you colour it?

WHO GOES THERE?

If A=1, B=2, C=3 and so on, work out which
dinosaur name is in each giant footprint.

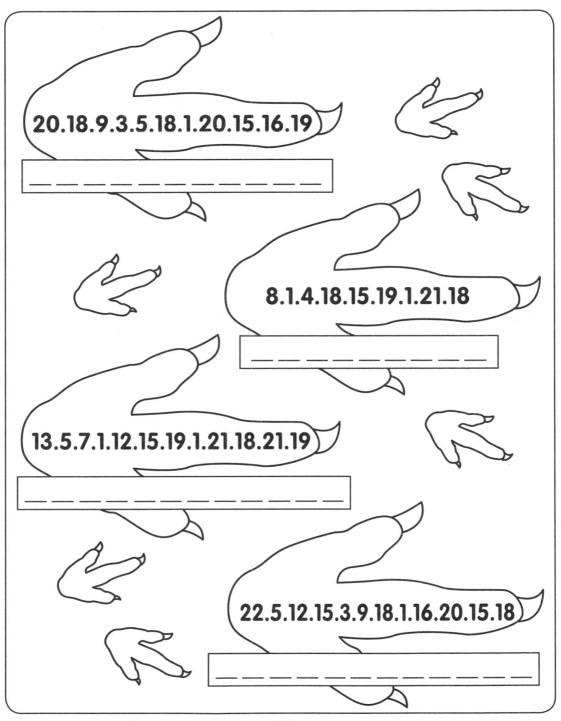

20.18.9.3.5.18.1.20.15.16.19

_ _ _ _ _ _ _ _ _ _ _

8.1.4.18.15.19.1.21.18

_ _ _ _ _ _ _ _ _

13.5.7.1.12.15.19.1.21.18.21.19

_ _ _ _ _ _ _ _ _ _ _ _ _

22.5.12.15.3.9.18.1.16.20.15.18

_ _ _ _ _ _ _ _ _ _ _

AGE OF THE DINOSAURS

How many smaller words can you make from the letters below?
Two are listed to get you started.

CRETACEOUS PERIOD

POST

CREASE

HAMMER HEAD

Watch out for Pachycephalosaurus' hard head as you colour him!

BONE DIGGERS

Match the squares to the main picture and write the correct grid reference for each one. One has been done to show you how.

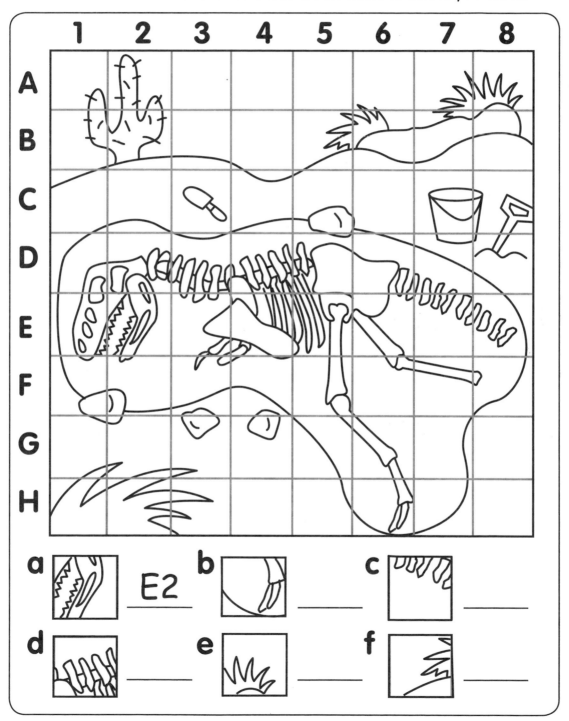

a — E2

b —

c —

d —

e —

f —

SEEING SPIRALS

Fit the three-letter words into the spaces to finish the names of four carnivorous dinosaurs.

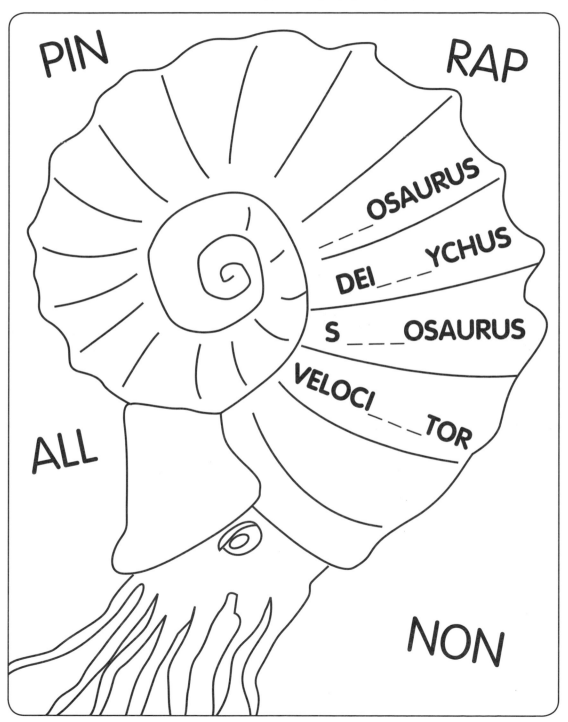

PIN

RAP

_ _ _ OSAURUS

DEI _ _ _ YCHUS

S _ _ _ OSAURUS

VELOCI _ _ _ TOR

ALL

NON

FLYING HIGH

These Archaeopteryx need colouring as they soar through the skies.

DINO-DOKU

Fill in the puzzle so that every row, column and
mini-grid has each of the four footprints.

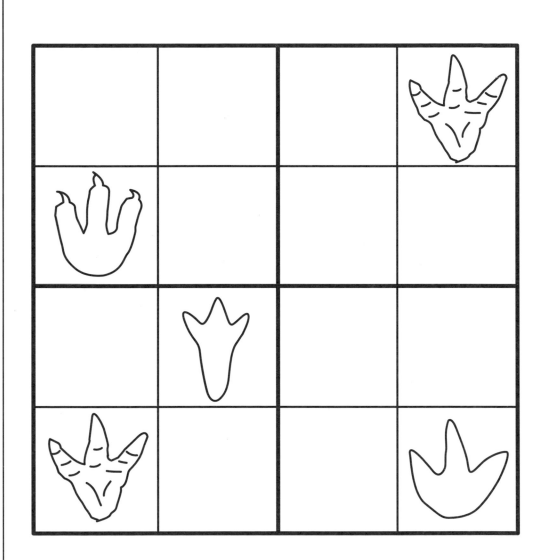

BIG MOUTH

Double the number each time to fill in
the spaces on T-rex's teeth.

POND LIFE

What colour will you make this pondersome plant-eater?

QUETZAL COUNT

How many Quetzalcoatlus are there
skimming across this page?

TERRIBLE TWINS

Which two T-rex are exactly the same?

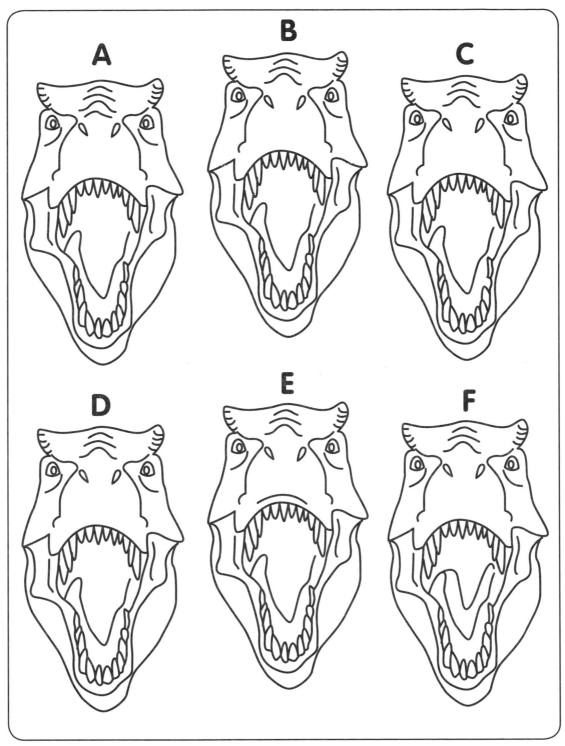

WATCH OUT!

Quickly, colour this Raptor before it runs away!

CREATURE COUNT

How many ammonites are swimming here?
And can you spot a tiny trilobite amongst them?

MONSTROUS MIX-UP

These dinosaurs all need labelling.
Can you match the names to the correct pictures?

Stegosaurus

Styracosaurus

Iguanodon

Ankylosaurus

T-rex

SUPER SPIKY

This horned dinosaur can be any colour you choose.

ONLY ODD

Solve the sums and use any answers that are odd
numbers to travel across the herd of Hypsilophodon.

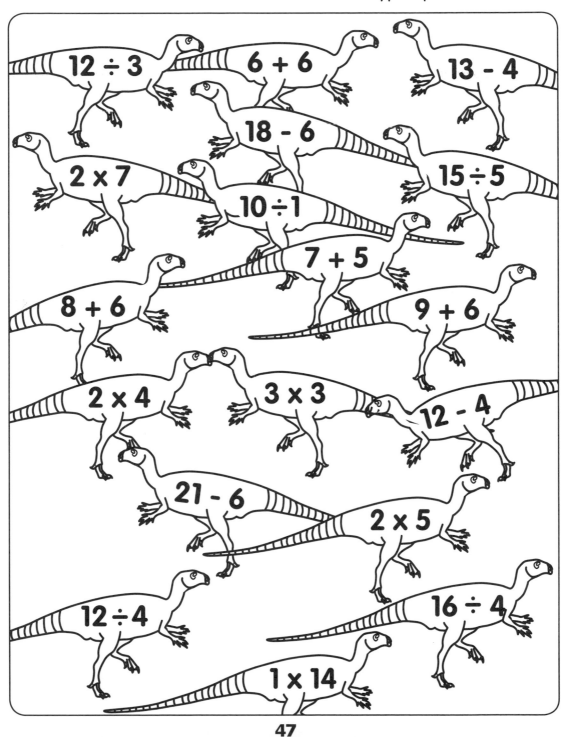

12 ÷ 3

6 + 6

13 - 4

18 - 6

2 x 7

15 ÷ 5

10 ÷ 1

7 + 5

8 + 6

9 + 6

2 x 4

3 x 3

12 - 4

21 - 6

2 x 5

12 ÷ 4

16 ÷ 4

1 x 14

FEATHERED DINOSAUR

Fill the feathers of this Caudipteryx in bright colours.

COMMON LINK

Cross out any C, M or N. The remaining letters spell a common link between the pictured dinosaurs.

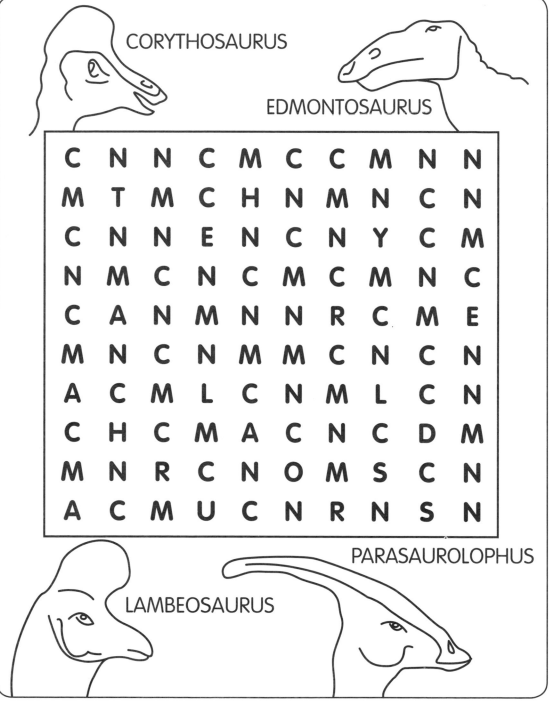

CORYTHOSAURUS

EDMONTOSAURUS

C	N	N	C	M	C	C	M	N	N
M	T	M	C	H	N	M	N	C	N
C	N	N	E	N	C	N	Y	C	M
N	M	C	N	C	M	C	M	N	C
C	A	N	M	N	N	R	C	M	E
M	N	C	N	M	M	C	N	C	N
A	C	M	L	C	N	M	L	C	N
C	H	C	M	A	C	N	C	D	M
M	N	R	C	N	O	M	S	C	N
A	C	M	U	C	N	R	N	S	N

PARASAUROLOPHUS

LAMBEOSAURUS

SIMPLY ENORMOUS

Write down every other letter, starting with A, to find the name of one of the biggest dinosaurs that ever lived.

‒ ‒ ‒ ‒ ‒ ‒ ‒ ‒ ‒ ‒ ‒ ‒ ‒ ‒ ‒

RUNNING AWAY

Where is this Heterodontosaurus headed? Colour it as it runs.

JURASSIC JOKE

Use the code to work out the answer to this joke.

What do you call an armoured dinosaur that's sleeping?

H G V T L - H M L I F H !

CODE

A	B	C	D	E	F	G	H	I	J	K	L	M	N
Z	**Y**	**X**	**W**	**V**	**U**	**T**	**S**	**R**	**Q**	**P**	**O**	**N**	**M**

O	P	Q	R	S	T	U	V	W	X	Y	Z
L	**K**	**J**	**I**	**H**	**G**	**F**	**E**	**D**	**C**	**B**	**A**

WEIGHTY EIGHTS

Which of the numbers on this mighty Torosaurus
are NOT in the eight times table?

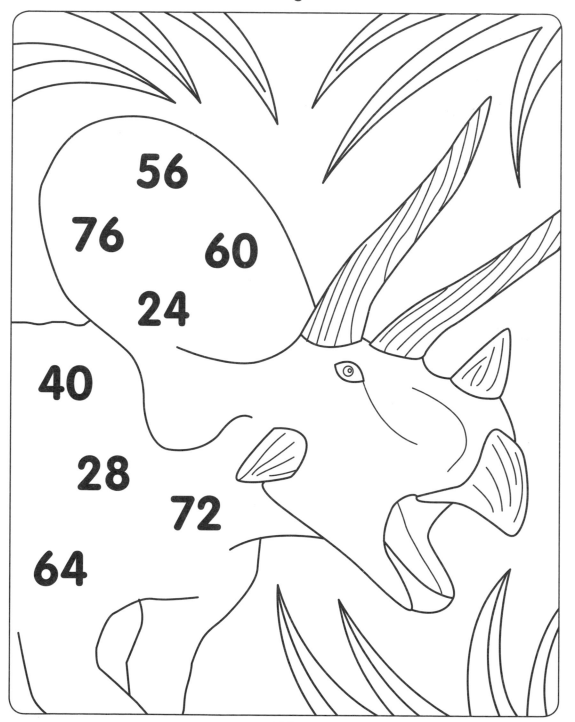

56

76

60

24

40

28

72

64

AMERICAN GIANT

Colour in this huge Alamosaurus, America's biggest dinosaur.

DINO TRACKER

Starting at C, find the listed dinosaur words
in a continuous trail through the grid.

AFROVENATOR

MINMI

BAGACERATOPS

C	O	M	P	A	U	R	O
N	G	O	S	S	B	S	L
A	P	A	R	A	A	U	O
T	S	E	V	O	G	H	P
H	U	N	A	R	A	C	E
M	R	O	T	F	A	S	R
I	I	B	Y	O	N	P	A
N	M	A	R	X	Y	O	T

PARASAUROLOPHUS

BARYONYX

COMPSOGNATHUS

BONE DIGGERS

Add some colour to this archaeological find.

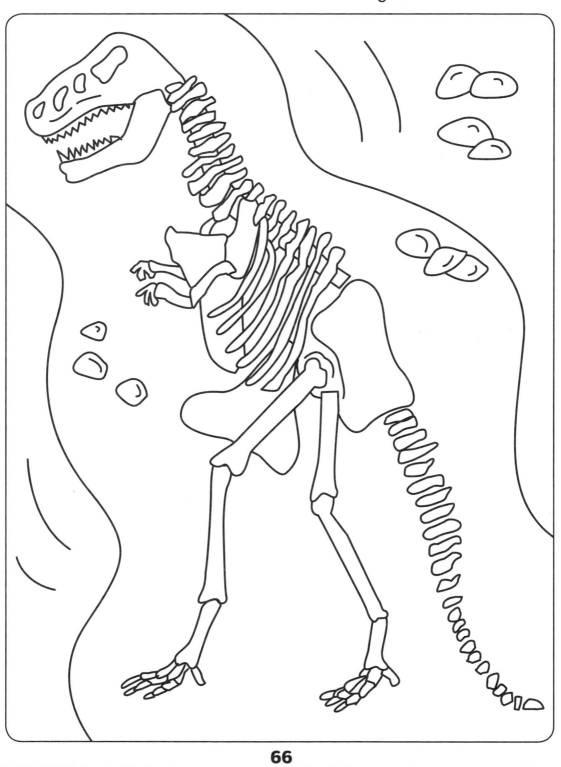

PROBLEMS, PROBLEMS

See if you can solve these maths problems without a calculator.

Libby is at the Dinosaur Museum shop. She has £5 and wants to buy a book that costs £2.50 and a poster that costs £3.50. Does she have enough money?

There are 30 people in Libby's class.
They need to split into 6 work groups.
How many children will be
in each group?

Half of Libby's class are boys. Five of the boys don't like dinosaurs. How many boys do like dinosaurs?

The class are at the museum from 10 o'clock until 2 o'clock. How much time do they have there?

If they have half an hour for lunch and one hour in a dino talk, how long do they have left to look around?

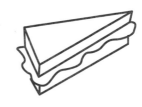

ON THE MOVE

Cross out every other letter, starting with D,
to find what has made these footprints.

DCTAYRANK
OUTAPTSO
REUXS

CLAWS AND SPIKES

These Kentrosaurus need some bright colours and patterns.

SCARY SWIMMERS

Can you spot eight differences between these
Plesiosaur pictures?

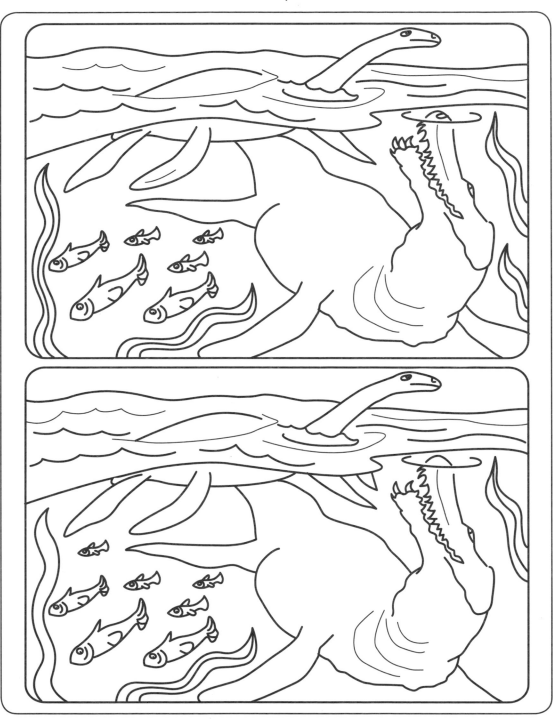

NAME CHANGE

Find out what Apatosaurus used to be called by decoding the message. The sides of the grid square tell you where to look, eg A = ⌟ while G = ⌞ . For example, S = ⌝

CRESTED CREATURE

Parasaurolophus may have been very noisy and colourful!

PERFECT TEN

This Tenontosaurus is hungry! Circle the sums
that have ten as the answer.

$100 \div 10$

$3\frac{1}{2} + 6\frac{1}{2}$

$4\frac{1}{2} + 6\frac{1}{2}$

$18 - 10$

$88 - 78$

$20 \div 10$

5×2

2×6

TAKE A LOOK

Which of these Gallimimus is not exactly
the same as the others?

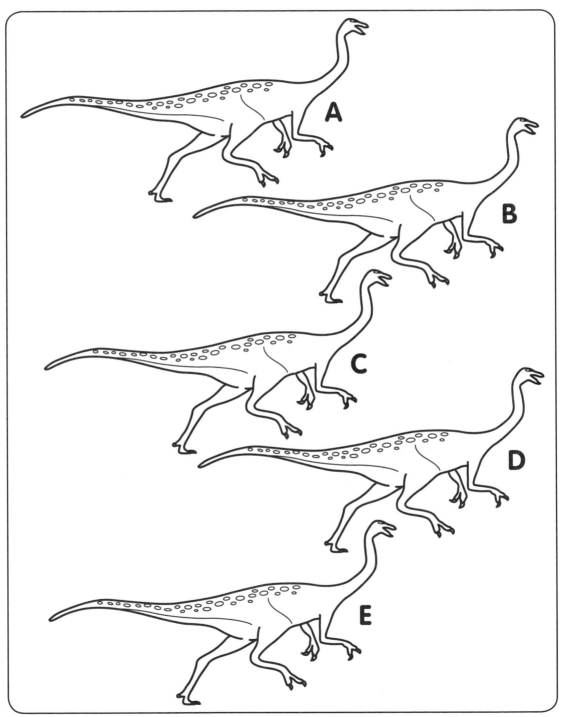

FOSSIL FIND

How many times can you find the word
CLAW hidden in the grid?

```
C L A C
L A W L C L
W C A L C A
A A L C L L
L C A W A L W
W C L W W C A L
C L A L A W C C
A A C L L A L A
L W L L L C W C L
L C A C L A W C A
C C L A C W A C L L
```

75

MEGA MATHS

Match up the plant eaters to the correct
answer for each sum.

36

11 x 3

32

50 – 13

Half of 64

34

37

12 + 22

33

6 x 6

ANSWERS

1. B and E

2.

4. 1. Bottom
   2. 3
   3. Right
   4. 4
   5. All of them!
   6. 2
   7. Left
   8. 2

5.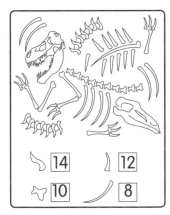

   14 12
   10 8

7.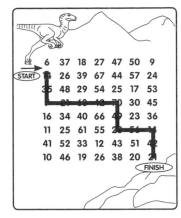

8. 45

10.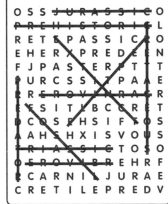

11. D

13. BARYONYX

B	A	R	O	S	A	U	R	U	S
A	L	L	O	S	A	U	R	U	S
U	T	A	H	R	A	P	T	O	R
E	O	T	Y	R	A	N	N	U	S
P	T	E	R	A	N	O	D	O	N
A	L	T	I	R	H	I	N	U	S
D	R	Y	O	S	A	U	R	U	S
X	I	A	O	S	A	U	R	U	S

14. TROODON

16. 1. ANKYLOSAURUS
    2. KENTROSAURUS
    3. PINACOSAURUS

19.

20. E

22.
```
        90
      40  50
    18  22  28
   8  10  12  16
  3   5   5   7   9
 2   1   4   1   6   3
```

23. KENTROSAURUS

25. GASTASEURUS

26. C

28. IT WAS A TRICERAHOPS

29. PALEONTOLOGIST

31. TRICERATOPS, HADROSAUR, MEGALOSAURUS, VELOCIRAPTOR

32. Here are some you might have thought of: poser, true, soup, root, sour, pore, route, tour, tired, ripe.

34. a) E2 b) H6 c) E7
    d) D4 e) A8 f) B5

35. ALLOSAURUS, DEINONYCHUS, SPINOSAURUS, VELOCIRAPTOR

37.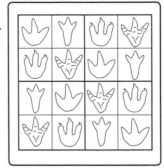

38. 2 4 8 16 32 64 128 252
    3 6 12 24 48 96 192 384

40. 12

41. B and D

43. 22

44.
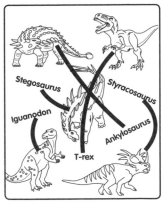

46.
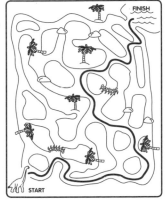

47.
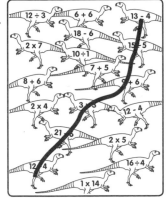

49. They are all hadrosaurs.

50. ARGENTINOSAURUS

52. STEGO-SNORUS!

53. 76, 60, 28

55.

56. Herrerasaurus was Triassic
    and 2.1m.
    Deinonychus was Cretaceous
    and 1.5m.
    Allosaurus was Jurassic and
    5m.

58. D

59. Seismosaurus was ENORMOUS!

61. BARYONYX

62.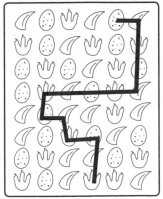

64.

65. MAIASAURA

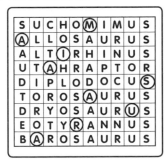

67. No

5

10

4 hours

2½ hours

68. CARNOTAURUS

70.

71. BRONTOSAURUS

73. $100 \div 10 = 10$

$3½ + 6½ = 10$

$88 - 78 = 10$

$5 \times 2 = 10$

74. C

75.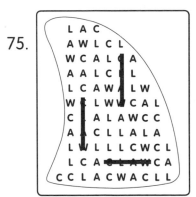

76. $11 \times 3 = 33$

$50 - 13 = 37$

Half of $64 = 32$

$12 + 22 = 34$

$6 \times 6 = 36$